GW00383389

Flute
Sight-reading
from 2018
ABRSM Grades 6–8

Contents

First published in 2017 by ABRSM (Publishing) Ltd, a wholly owned subsidiary of ABRSM
© 2017 by The Associated Board of the Royal Schools of Music
Unauthorized photocopying is illegal

Music origination by Katie Johnston
Cover by Kate Benjamin & Andy Potts
Printed in England by Halstan & Co. Ltd, Amersham, Bucks., on materials from sustainable sources
P14523

Grade 6

Lazy Days

Contrasts

At the Fairground

Fandango

Grade 6

Evening Tide

Dreaming

Juggling

Swing Cool

Grade 6

Mini Minuet

Circus Skills

Memories

Gigue

Grade 6

Direct Flight

Whirlwind

Strolling By

Walk Don't Run

Grade 6

Five Jive

Fiesta

Cat and Mouse

Playtime

Grade 7

Capriccioso

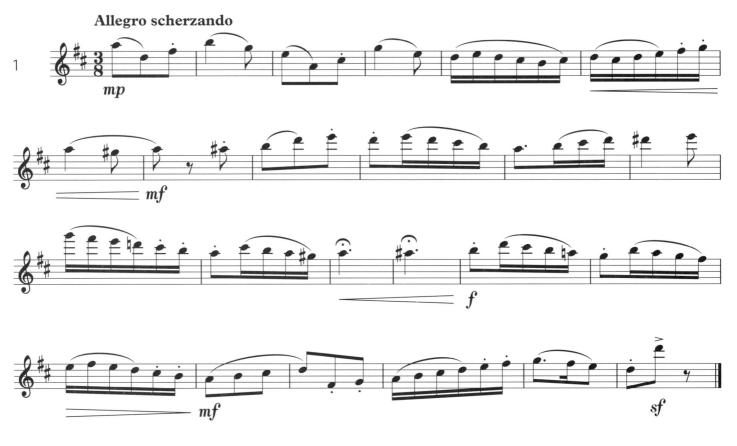

Questions and Answers

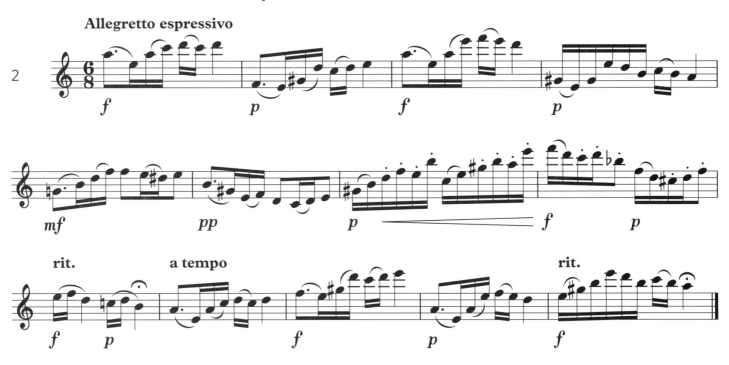

Sliding Doors

The River in Autumn

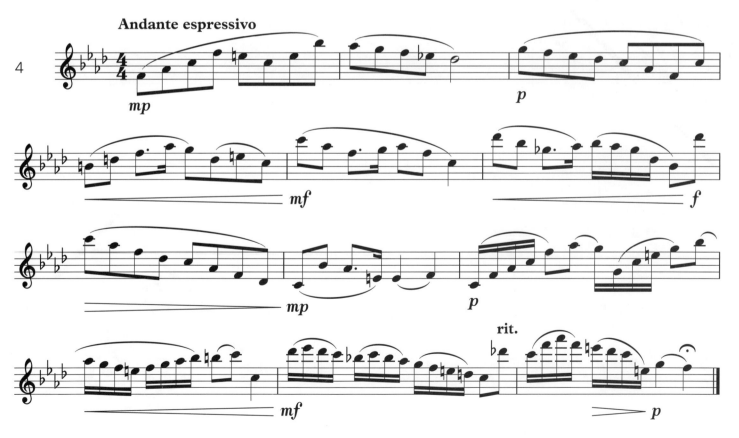

Grade 7

Aria

Hat Dance

Solemn Serenade

Princess's Song

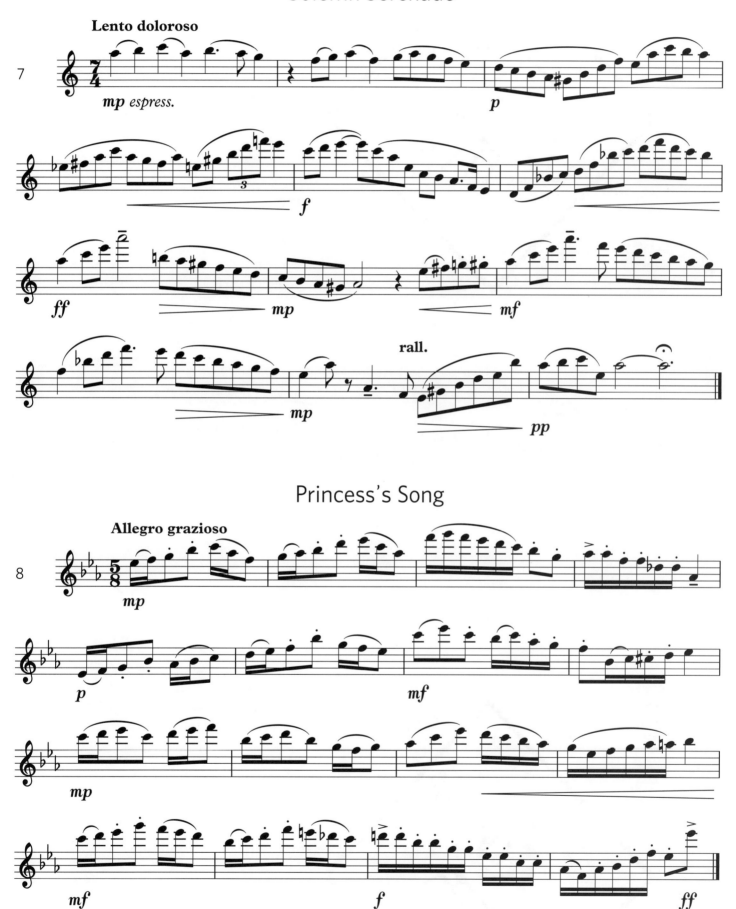

Grade 7

First Love

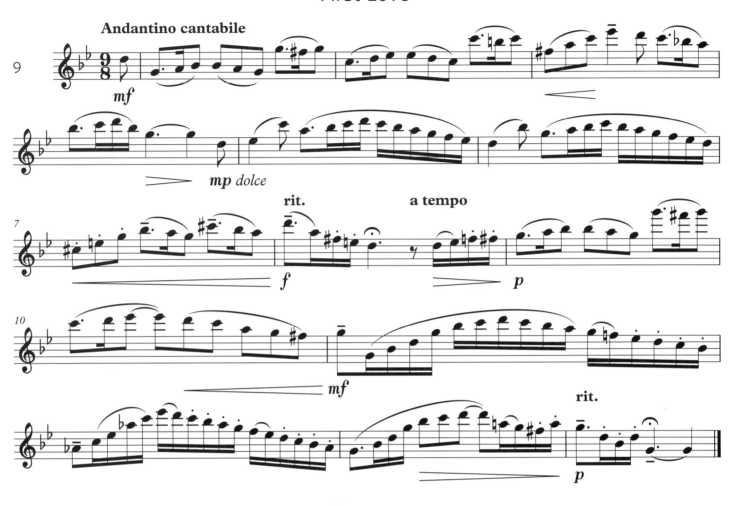

Time Flies

Fly a Kite

Lightning Strikes

Grade 7

Pave the Way

Andante ritmico

13

Those Were the Days

Lento doloroso

14

Free Wheeling

Rain Dance

Grade 7

Easy Street

Spring Song

Catch Me if You Can

Swinging Along

Grade 8

Lament

1

Playground

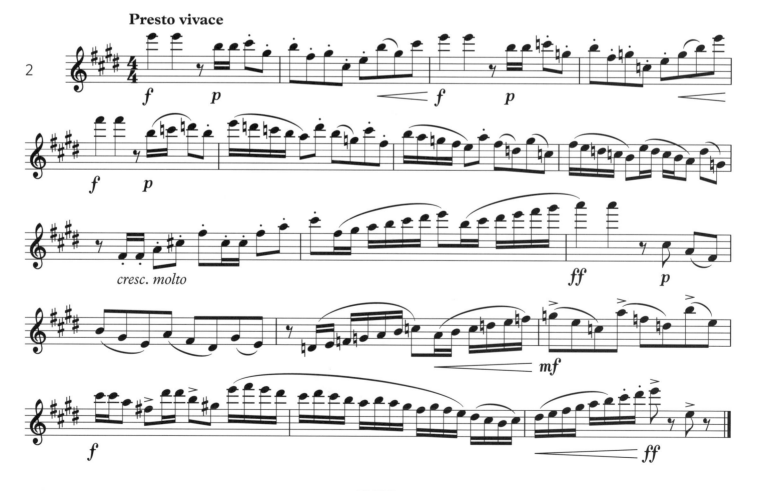

2

Autumn Blues

Heart to Heart

Grade 8

Folk Song

Night Club

Highland Fling

Perpetuum Mobile

Grade 8

Sicilienne

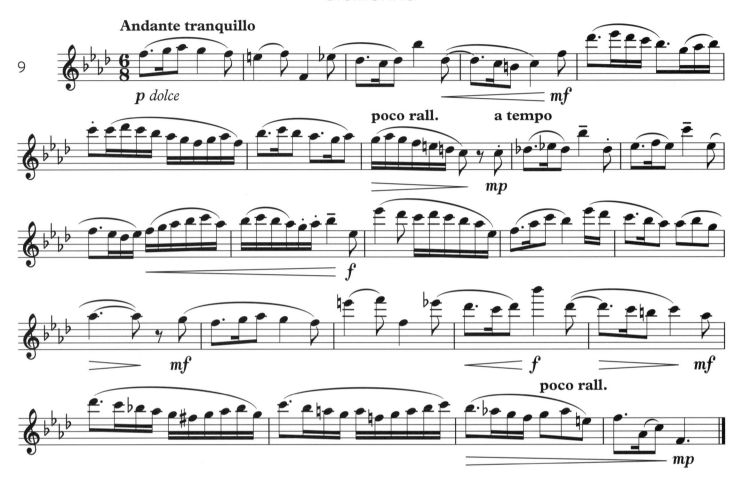

Cat Among the Pigeons

A Little Day Music

March

Grade 8

Topsy-turvy

13

Prairie Dance

14

Pulling a Thread

Carnival Rag

Grade 8

Jack-in-the-Box

17

An Evening in Paris

18

Mists of Time

19

Weeping Willow

20